The Story of
Shadrach, Meshach, and Abednego

By Rhonda Colburn

Illustrated by Gwen Connelly

IDEALS CHILDREN'S BOOKS
Nashville, Tennessee

ATTENTION: SCHOOLS AND CORPORATIONS
This book is available at quantity discount with bulk purchases
for educational, fund-raising, business, or premium use. For infor-
mation, please write to Special Sales Department, P.O. Box
140300, Nashville, TN 37214.

A Word to Parents and Friends

This story is one of a series of biblical stories especially written, illustrated, and designed to explain a difficult concept in a gentle and simple manner.

Even the youngest child will understand the timeless lesson inherent in each bible story. Most of all, preschoolers, beginning readers, and older children will enjoy hearing and reading these accounts of heroes from one of the oldest and most exciting books of all: the Holy Bible.

Long, long ago the king of Babylon, Nebuchadnezzar, attacked and conquered the city of Jerusalem. Nebuchadnezzar ordered his soldiers to capture children from the royal household. He told his soldiers to take only the children who were bright and healthy. Among the children taken to Babylon were three young boys.

Nebuchadnezzar wanted these boys to learn all about Babylon. They were to learn to read and write the language of their new country and were given new Babylonian names. The three young boys were now called Shadrach, Meshach, and Abednego.

Shadrach, Meshach, and Abednego lived in the king's palace and were given the same rich food that the king ate. But the king's food was not prepared according to God's laws. If the boys ate this rich food, they would be breaking the laws God gave to their people, the Israelites.

"Please," they asked the chief guard, "may we have plain food such as vegetables instead of this food that our God has forbidden us to eat?"

The guard wanted to grant their request, but he was afraid that the boys would grow weak if they didn't eat the rich food. If they became sick, the king would be very angry at the guard.

Then the boys asked, "Please give us simple food that will not be against God's laws. Let us eat this for ten days. Then compare us to the other captives who eat the king's food."

The official agreed and gave the boys the food that they wanted.

At the end of ten days, Shadrach, Meshach, and Abednego looked healthier than any of the others, so the chief official gave them all the simple food and vegetables they wanted.

Shadrach, Meshach, and Abednego studied hard for several years, and God blessed them and gave them knowledge and skill in all kinds of learning. At the end of that time, the king sent for the three friends and was very pleased with them. He saw that they knew ten times more than his brightest advisers. Shadrach, Meshach, and Abednego became rulers in Babylon.

One day King Nebuchadnezzar decided to build a golden idol in Babylon. The idol was ninety feet high and nine feet wide. When it was finished, the king ordered all the rulers and governors in Babylon to come worship the idol. This order included Shadrach, Meshach, and Abednego. Soon hundreds of people stood before the idol Nebuchadnezzar had built.

A herald stood to announce the king's laws to the crowd. "When you hear the sound of the horns, flutes, harps, pipes, and other music," he cried to the people, "you must fall down and worship the idol. Whoever does not fall down and worship the idol will be thrown into the fiery furnace! This is the commandment given by the king himself."

So when the people heard the sound of the horns, flutes, harps, pipes, and other music, they fell to the ground and worshiped the idol.

That is, everyone fell down except Shadrach, Meshach, and Abednego. They knew that there was only one true God. If they worshiped an idol, they would be breaking the law God gave them which said, "You will have no other God but me."

Some wicked men looked up and saw that Shadrach, Meshach, and Abednego would not worship the idol. These men ran to King Nebuchadnezzar.

"O King," they cried, "you have commanded that when the people hear the sound of the horns, flutes, harps, pipes, and other music, they are to fall down and worship the idol. But the Israelite rulers, Shadrach, Meshach, and Abednego, are not paying attention to your laws. They will not worship the idol!"

Nebuchadnezzar was furious. He demanded that Shadrach, Meshach, and Abednego be brought to him. "Is it true that you will not worship the idol that I have built? When you hear the sound of the horns, flutes, harps, pipes, other music, you will worship my idol or you will be thrown into the fiery furnace! And who is your God who will save you from me?" he shouted angrily.

But the three men refused. "We will not worship your idol," they said. "We worship the true God. If you throw us into the fiery furnace, we will not be afraid. Our God will save us, O King."

Nebuchadnezzar grew even angrier. He ordered his men to heat the furnace seven times hotter than it was before. Then he ordered his strongest soldiers to tie up Shadrach, Meshach, and Abednego and throw them into the flames.

As the soldiers threw Shadrach, Meshach, and Abednego into the roaring furnace, the heat from the flames was so great that the mighty soldiers were killed instantly.

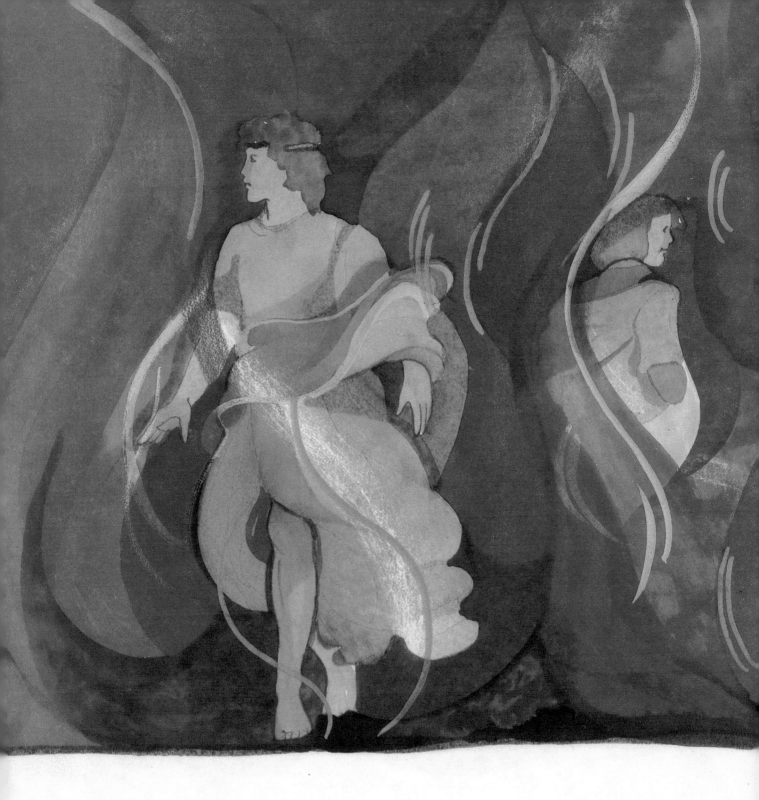

As he gazed into the furnace, King Nebuchadnezzar suddenly leaped to his feet in surprise. "My soldiers threw three men into the fire, but now I see four men walking around inside the furnace!" he cried. "They are all untied and unhurt, and the fourth man looks like the Son of God!"

The king walked to the opening of the furnace and called to the three men. "Shadrach, Meshach, Abednego! Servants of the Most High God, come out!"

And Shadrach, Meshach, and Abednego walked out of the fire, completely unhurt by the heat and flames.

All the king's officials gathered around them. "Look," they said in amazement, "Shadrach, Meshach, and Abednego are not harmed at all! Their clothing isn't burned in the least. Why, they don't even smell like smoke!"

Then King Nebuchadnezzar praised God and said, "Great is the God of Shadrach, Meshach, and Abednego! He has sent his angel to protect them and has saved them from the flames because they would rather face death than worship any god but their own God. Anyone who speaks against the God of Shadrach, Meshach, and Abednego will be severely punished. No other God can do such great things for his people."